Borderline Visible
by Ant Hampton
77 min

I wasn't alone

It wasn’t the first time
we’d set out on this kind of trip together.

We weren't alone

# *Collected Poems*

*1909–1962*

It wasn't the first time
we'd set out on this kind of trip together.

the last time

couldn't look

somehow

to be taken

care

maybe help

eyes fell

much thought

upside-down
photocopies of a poem

With the smell of hyacinths across the garden
Recalling things that other people have desired.
Are these ideas right or wrong?

III

The October night comes down: returning as before
Except for a slight sensation of being ill at ease
I mount the stairs and turn the handle of the door
And feel as if I had mounted on my hands and knees.
'And so you are going abroad; and when do you return?
But that's a useless question.
You hardly know when you are coming back,
You will find so much to learn.'
My smile falls heavily among the bric-à-brac.

'Perhaps you can write to me.'
My self-possession flares up for a second;
*This* is as I had reckoned.
'I have been wondering frequently of late
(But our beginnings never know our ends!)
Why we have not developed into friends.'
I feel like one who smiles, and turning shall remark
Suddenly, his expression in a glass.
My self-possession gutters; we are really in the dark.

'For everybody said so, all our friends,
They all were sure our feelings would relate
So closely! I myself can hardly understand.
We must leave it now to fate.
You will write, at any rate.
Perhaps it is not too late.

part of me

probably

calm

deep

vortex

murmur

solace

tangle

survival

if it doesn't hurt

ERLANDS
Berlin
3D
JM
GERMANY
CZE
REPU
Munich
3D
AUSTR

THE INNER LI
IRGENDWO
hin

A little life with dried tubers.
Summer surprised us, coming over the Starnbergersee
With a shower of rain; we stopped in the colonnade,
And went on in sunlight, into the Hofgarten,
And drank coffee, and talked for an hour.
Bin gar keine Russin, stamm' aus Litauen, echt deutsch.

BREXI
SODEMaction.co.uk

Puppen & Bären
Manufaktur

Also... Wir sind neu in Deutschland
und wollen Deutsch lernen.
Wir kennen bisher nicht viele Wörter;
eigentlich nur die, die wir gerade sprechen.

Wir haben diese Worte
auswendig gelernt, wir beide.

Wir wollen Deutsch lernen,
mit Beispielen, was Leute
wirklich sagen, und nicht,
was Lehrbücher behaupten,
was Leute sagen würden.

The text in German (pp. 20–23) was learnt by heart and spoken to drivers while hitch hiking randomly through Germany over 7 days, for the project Mouth Piece (Mund-Stück), 2018. Translation:

So... we're new in Germany and we want to learn German.
We don't know so many words yet;
actually only what we're saying right now.

We learnt these words by heart.

We want to learn German with examples of what people
really say, and not what textbooks say people say.

Would you mind if we asked you a question?

And could we record your answers?
Only the sound, no image. The recording is
for us because we probably won't understand
what you're saying, while you're speaking.

We'll listen to it later, and then learn what you say by heart.

Ok, here's the question.

What, in your opinion, needs to be said?

# Würde es Ihnen etwas ausmachen, wenn wir Ihnen eine Frage stellen?

**dumb question**
(Hello, we want to learn this language so, obviously, we need examples of what really needs to be said. Those are the words we want, not any old rubbish.)

*"Dumb is an ill-prepared slacker, riding on hunches and intuition. Wilfully amnesiac—History, what's that?—dumb is a tabula rasa, full of emptiness. Caring little for progress or narrative, dumb moves laterally, occasionally spiraling back in on itself. "Dumb ... favors re-recontext-ualization", reframing, redoing, remixing, recycling—rather than having to go through the effort of creating something from scratch. Dumb embraces the messiness of contradiction and revels in the beauty of the ridiculously obvious. Trading on the mundane and common, dumb plays a low-stakes game. Since dumb has nothing to lose, dumb owes nothing to anyone, and in that way it is free.*
*Smart struts. Dumb stumbles. Smart dazzles. Dumb numbs."*
From Kenneth Goldsmith's essay, *'Being Dumb'*.

**das wird man doch wohl noch sagen dürfen!**
While conceiving the project we were introduced to this expression, which roughly translates as "Surely it's ok to say that!": a right-wing, populist catchphrase apparently being instrumentalised for the unleashing of demons that had been more or less contained for decades through moderation, anti-nationalism and guilt.

Often, your initial reaction to our question was confusion — "Um welches Thema?" (what do you mean - what about?) — but when you understood that your convictions might be called for, we received either a straight-up rant or, more commonly, a uniquely complex attempt at articulating two things at once: your convictions, and a signalling of your awareness that to rant about them would be dangerous.
The speech-acts resulting from an attempt to balance these two elements seemed to us to contain something unique to Germany's national consciousness, and was the main reason why we decided to learn not just what you said, but how you said it.

**Und–könnten wir Ihre Antworten aufnehmen? Nur den Ton, nicht das Bild. Die Aufnahme ist nur für uns, da wir wahrscheinlich erst einmal nicht verstehen werden, was Sie sagen, während Sie sprechen.**

**Wir hören uns dann später die Aufnahme an, und lernen Ihre Worte auswendig.**

**Ok, hier ist die Frage.**

**responsbility**

We'll learn by heart what you say. We invite you to write into us, something like an internal tattoo, but alive: a text in voice form (there used to be no difference). We tell you we're doing this in order to learn German. In other words, your words will become representative of the German language.

If there's a desire to say what you feel needs to be said, is that tempered in any way by this knowledge? Does the fact that we simply will not understand what you're saying until much later make any difference to what you decide to say? Is there a sense of responsibility, and could it relate to, or dovetail with, the concrete fact of you being responsible now in this moment, as a driver?

**author's rights**

We don't tell you that we might use what you say for an artwork (let's not get bogged down in conversations about art—a subject that could easily cause misunderstanding or division). We think that's Ok, because we tell you very clearly that, with your agreement, we'll record your words and then learn them by heart. The implication of that is of a secondary recording, an embedding of your words and voice inside us. Do you really expect it to stay there? In German, 'by heart' is 'auswendig' which breaks down to *wendig*, 'a turn' + *aus*, 'to the outside'—"here used in the sense of 'externally,' i.e., 'without looking into a book'" *(Etymological Dictionary of the German Language).* Every process of learning involves an interiorization but it must be obvious that somewhere, sometime, somehow, your words are going to reappear in the world.

**thinking time**

eh, eh, Ach so, ja, * eh, eh, ih, ich kann darauf schlecht antworten, weil ich mir darüber noch keine Gedanken gemacht habe! Was so, eh, in mir vorgeht, eh, ja, eh, was...

## Was müsste Ihrer Meinung nach mal gesagt werden?

0"Er, er, oh, I see, yes, er, er, I, I can't answer that very well, because I haven't thought about it yet! What's going on inside me, er, yes, er, what..."

We wanted to say, take your time, but you did anyway. You're not in any hurry, you're driving. We hoped you could trust us to listen to you thinking-through-speaking, or as Mladen Dolar elucidates, by way of Kleist,** speaking-to-think. But we needn't have worried—it seems part of the deal with hitching is that each side takes a radical leap and trusts the other.

We were concerned that our silence would be oppressive, but again, driving helps; with eyes ahead on the road and no need to look us in the face, it's almost like being on the analyst's couch. Even better, perhaps, with those landscapes going by. Those landscapes. When it came to memorizing your answers, we found images hard-wired into the words. Every time we speak them, visuals of what went by while the words came out of *your* mouths are reprojected onto our mental retinas.

**narcissism and authenticity**
At times opinions are brandished like trophies. To have one makes you feel good, confident, ready to be heard. Social events (or networks—"What's on your mind, Ant?") seem often to demand a performance of one's thoughts within a sphere where the step between 'thought' and 'opinion' can be small enough for some not to notice, others to trip over. If you don't have an opinion, or if you worry the ones you do have are too old, you might feel the urge to go out and get a new one—off the shelf, as it were.

Are these really your words? We transparently tell you of our intention to learn what you say by heart. But has something like that already happened here? Where did you get these ideas, these words? Are your hesitations coming from an attempt to articulate your own thoughts, or are you trying to mentally re-download something you read, or heard?

**an opinion — for what?**

Sometimes we sensed our question brought focus to the economies of confidence and hopelessness that probably define society more than anything else. The men in this snack bar had long since given up on being listened to, and their answer was strikingly honest:

Greussen ist eine (is' 'ne) Kl-Kleinstadt, ist ei... e—n... nichts!
S' is' nichts! Greussen ist eine - kann man Deutsch reden, gell?
-tote Stadt. Nichts los. Absolut. Hier gibt's nichts.
Keine Insf-Infrastruktur, gar nichts (gornix).
Nur Discounter Supermärkte... kleine Betriebe.
eine Meinung, für was?

"Greussen is a s-small town, it's a... a n-nothing! It's nothing!
Greussen is a—I can speak German right?—dead town.
Nothing going on. Absolutely nothing. There's nothing here.
No infrastructure, nothing. Just discount supermarkets, small businesses.
An opinion—for what?"

**anything goes**

Clichés, recycled tropes, obscenities, banalities, indulgence, nonsense or complete misunderstandings—we were ready for anything, figuring that as long as there was something at stake for you behind the impulse to speak, any utterance should contain the energies and between-the-lines 'culture' that would, for us, make it worth learning by heart.

```
Well b… I, I, I'd say get the Wall back.
Bring the Wall back. Yep.
Bring the Wall back. Should put it back up.
There was no problem then.
Everyone was insured. There was no unemployment.
```

Audio edit and notebook excerpt,
Mouth Piece (Mund-Stück), 2018

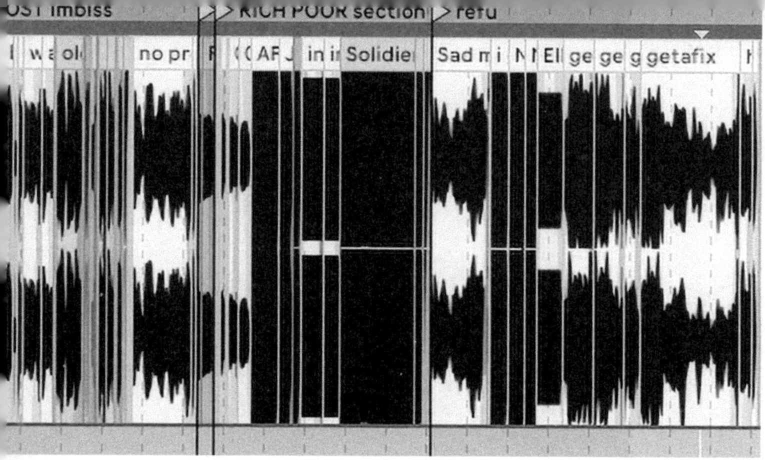


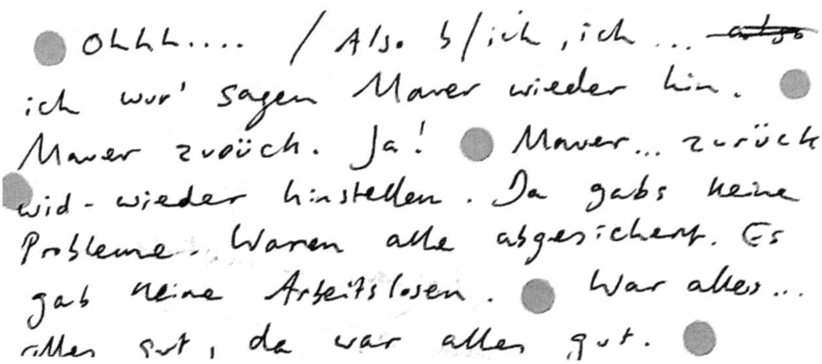


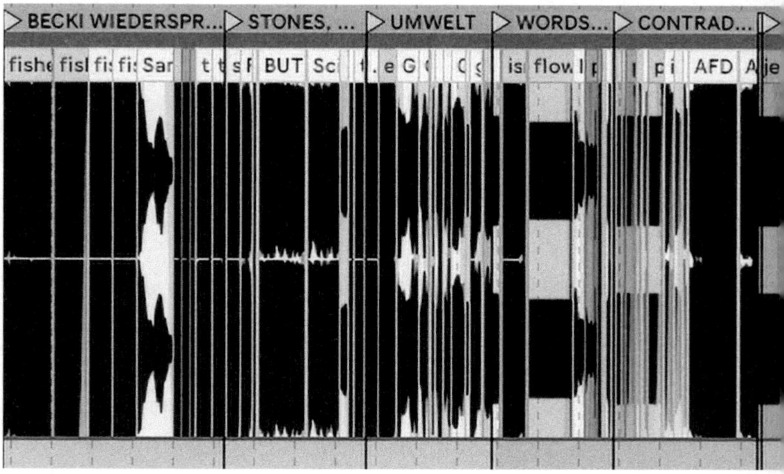


* ● = take a breath. Text taken from script for learning. Represented over the page by red dots (image taken from notebook).

** Heinrich von Kleist, “Über die allmähliche Verfertigung der Gedanken beim Reden” (“On the Gradual Production of Thoughts through Speech”).

just starting

to hear

we shouldn't

but

but

never

chose

endless

whirlpool

passing the stages

no longer

defiance

drifting

strangers

FIG. 128.—Israelitas españoles, vendedores de naranjas y semillas

spiralling

wider

now, there

'cuando el vapor está yanashayando al iskele de Büyükada,
va tamar un hamal que tasheyades los bavules'.
Its grammatical structure remains Spanish, but there
are many loan-words and verbs from other languages.
It was belittled and was perceived
as a 'salad' more than a proper tongue.
At the time, a nationalist campaign 'Citizen Speak
Turkish!' caused anxiety within the community.
I remember telling myself: 'I'll master Turkish
so perfectly that everyone will admire me'.

Rita

> ant
> Sa langue, le djudyó/ladino/ djudezmo ou judéo-espagnol...

This whole language ambivalence and flexibilité is so fascinating

I can see how karaoke in ladino can become a very interesting experimental practice for us and also I'm taking notes of every ladino expression my grandma used to say
-ainaras que no té caiga
- la bojora
-masharla
-el tatele
- caparà!
- schleper

But Tanpınar, with his **poetics of the indolent flaneur,** rejects the social-realist tradition that was dominant in Turkey...
He seems to have taken to heart Baudelaire's dictum that the modern artist is "the painter of both the passing moment and everything in that moment that smacks of eternity." He lingers defiantly on classic Istanbul scenes: ferries with melancholy foghorns and broken marble fountains.

ant

11:37

Sa langue, le djudyó/ladino/ djudezmo ou judéo-espagnol d'Orient qui est la seule porte d'accès à sa littérature, peu ou pas traduite, est l'objet d'attaques et d'atteintes constantes depuis la fin du 19e siècle dont la réhispanisation n'est pas la moindre.

L'une des manières dont elle répond à cette pression, c'est en cultivant sa polyréférencialité : plurilingue, flexible, se conformant aux lois du pays et à celles du judaïsme, elle joue de la multiplicité de ses facettes et de son adaptabilité en fonction du contexte. Certains traits qui lui sont propres font parfois l'objet de dissimulation ou de déni. C'est le cas par exemple de sa politique complexe d'intégration de membres étrangers à la communauté, bien plus tolérante que dans d'autres traditions juives, ancienne et tout aussi fondée en droit ; ou de la pratique très intériorisée de la kashrut qui peut être visible par les siens et invisible aux autres ;

The Peripatetic school, founded by Aristotle,[2] was actually known simply as the Peripatos.[3] Aristotle's school came to be so named because of the *peripatoi* ("walkways", some covered or with colonnades) of the Lyceum where the members met.[4] The legend that the name came from Aristotle's alleged habit of walking while lecturing may have started with Hermippus of Smyrna.[5]

Nous sommes un monstre privé de sens
Nous sommes hors douleur
Et nous avons perdu
Presque la langue à l'étranger.[9]

We are a "monster" void of sense
outside sorrow
e nearly lost
gue in foreign lands.

allusion to the tongue lost
ck too quickly to the
'monster.'"

I can connect
Nothing with nothing.
The broken fingernails of dirty hands.
My people humble people who expect
Nothing.'

la la

To Carthage then I

The people in this war-ridden erritory are almost continually ubject to famine, exposure, and even worse dangers.

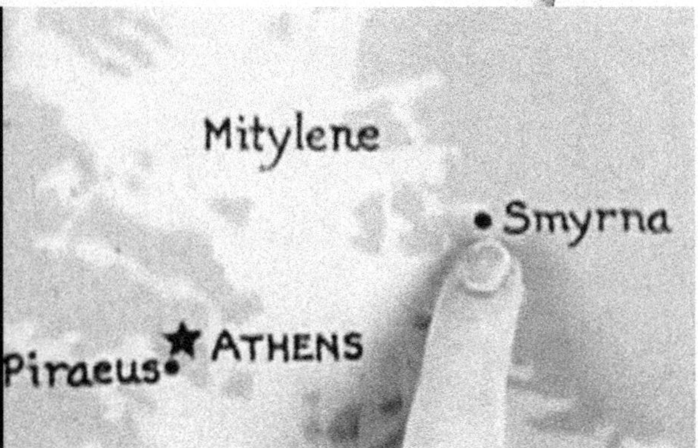

Otranto (Italy), 13 May 2020

O the moon shone bright on Mrs. Porter
And on her daughter
They wash their feet in soda water
*Et O ces voix d'enfants, chantant dans la coupole!*

Twit twit twit

AIA DEI TURCHI

And other withered stumps of time

the nearby 'Baia dei Turchi', 13 May 2020

CANLI
MİDİLLİ
NİKARYA
23:57
SON DAKİKA

SON DAKİKA
CANLI
HABER TÜRK
TÜRKİYE
GELİRE ENDEKSLİ SENET İHRACI
KUPON ÖDEMELERİNDE GETİRİ GARANTİSİ OLACAK
23:57
SON DAKİKA
BİN LİRANIN ÜZERİNDEKİ TUTARLAR İÇİN 12 AY OLARAK BEL
1,020.717

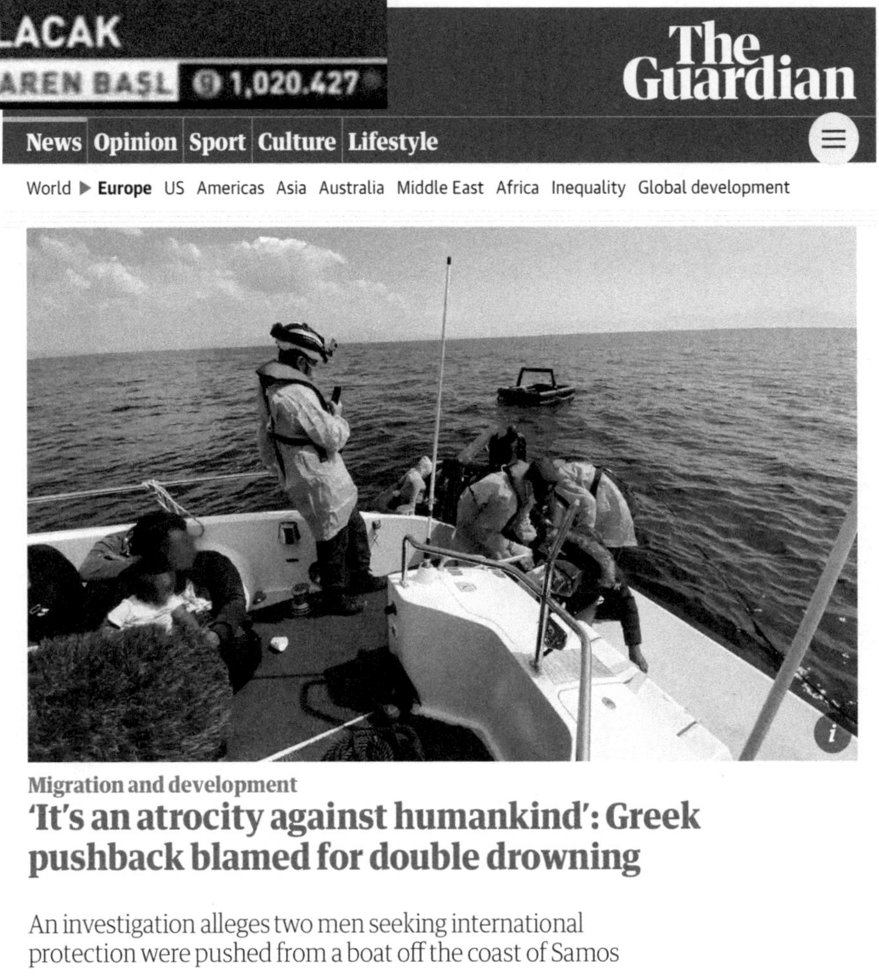
The Guardian

News Opinion Sport Culture Lifestyle

World ▶ **Europe** US Americas Asia Australia Middle East Africa Inequality Global development

Migration and development

## 'It's an atrocity against humankind': Greek pushback blamed for double drowning

An investigation alleges two men seeking international protection were pushed from a boat off the coast of Samos

After the torchlight red on sweaty faces

**Katy Fallon** *in Samos*

Thu 17 Feb 2022 08.00 GMT

On 15 September 2021, Sidy Keita from Ivory Coast and Didier Martial Kouamou Nana from Cameroon, boarded a dinghy from Turkey to Greece. Despite making it to the Greek island of Samos, their bodies were found days later, washed ashore in Aydin province, on the Aegean coast.

Interviews with more than a dozen witnesses, analysis of classified documents, satellite imagery, social media accounts and online material, and discussions with officials in Turkey and Greece, have helped piece together what happened over five September days during which the two men died, likely victims of a pushback by the Greek authorities.

What happened to these men, who left their homes to escape political oppression and for a better life overseas, has been investigated by the Guardian, Lighthouse Reports, Mediapart and Der Spiegel.

The Greek prime minister, Kyriakos Mitsotakis, has frequently denied that pushbacks occur. But there is mounting evidence that would-be asylum seekers are being illegally removed from Greek territory before having the chance to lodge asylum applications.

Keita, 36, left Ivory Coast after taking part in protests against president Alassane Ouattara. He arrived in Turkey in March 2020. Kouamou, 33, a mechanic in Cameroon, landed in Turkey last year, hoping to join his brother who had been living in France since 2014.

Like many before them, both men went to the Basmane district of Izmir, a known spot for people who want to be smuggled into Europe. They were among 36 who then boarded a dinghy from near Kusadasi on the Turkish coast in the early hours of 15 September.

> **We have to denounce this because it's inhuman. They hit people in front of us, they traumatised the children**

According to testimonies, the boat arrived at the north-eastern shore of Samos around 7am, just as the sun was rising. The area, Cape Prasso, is a peninsula with steep hillsides and perilous drops to the water.

Lawyers working for the Human Rights Legal Project (HRLP) on Samos, 10km from Cape Prasso, received a text from an unknown number informing them of the dinghy's arrival, with photos taken from land of a Greek coastguard vessel spotted in the area. At 10.25am, the HRLP emailed local police, the UN refugee agency UNHCR, a member of the European Commission based on the island and the Reception and Identification service for asylum seekers on Samos, informing them of the arrival.

The HRLP email, seen by the Guardian, asks that the arrivals be provided with the necessary assistance to register as asylum seekers on the island as prescribed by law. There was no reply.

Shortly after the dinghy arrived, witnesses describe hearing what sounded like shots being fired. In a panic, the people on the dinghy split up, scrambling up the hilly terrain to hide where they could. Eight managed to escape into the countryside but the other 28, including a baby, young children and a pregnant woman, were apprehended by the authorities. That afternoon, it is claimed they were loaded on to a coastguard boat, driven out to sea and cast adrift on two life rafts, a well-documented form of pushback by Greek authorities.

Jean* and at least two others were allegedly strip-searched and beaten. Jean said at least one woman was subjected to an internal physical search by officers looking for money. "The police beat us with the greatest violence," he said. "I was punched in the face and in the stomach. I was crying." Pascaline* said she was robbed of her money and her baby was thrown into the life raft "as if you were throwing a garbage can".

"We have to denounce this because it's inhuman. They hit people in front of us, they traumatised the children."

The two rafts were picked up by the Turkish coastguard a few hours later. The pregnant woman had gone into labour on the raft and delivered her baby shortly after being rescued.

Of the eight people who initially escaped the authorities in Samos, four would make it to a refugee camp on the island, while the other four were picked up. One woman was apprehended outside a monastery, given a bottle of water and cast out to sea on her own. She was rescued by the Turkish coastguard on 17 September.

### The Samos pushback

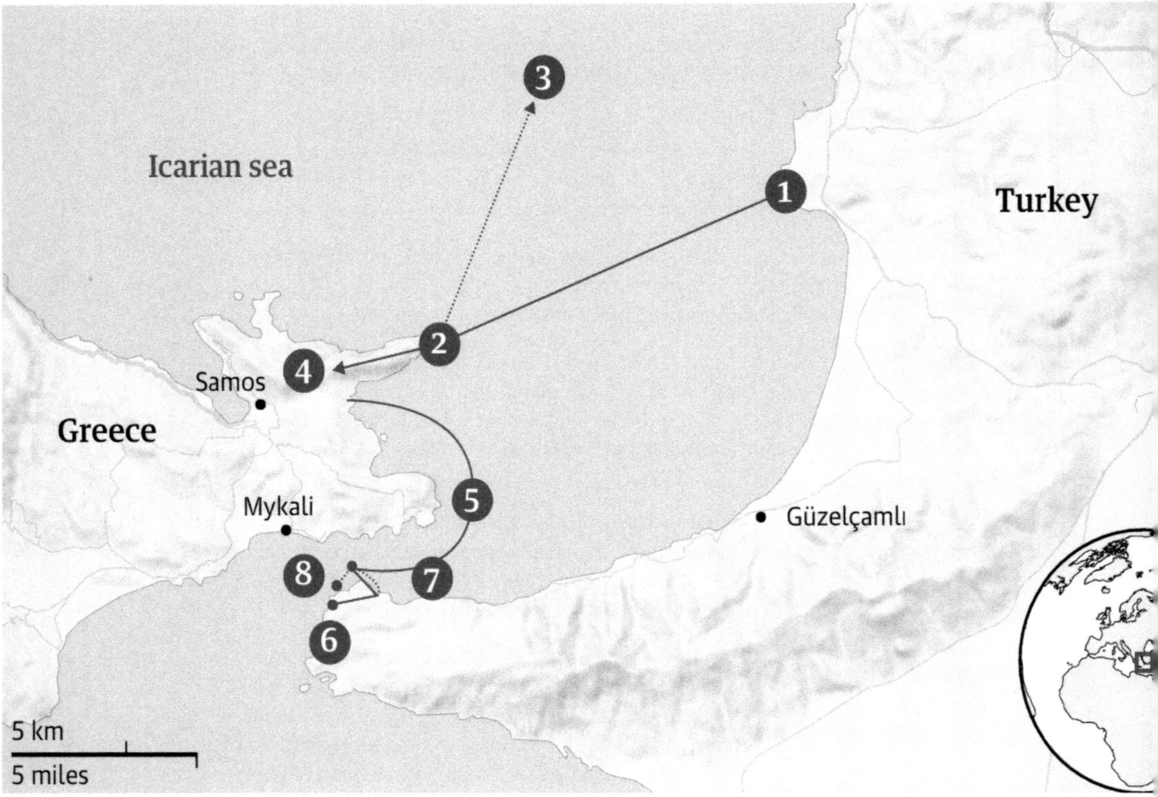


1. **15 September** A group of 36 people leaves Turkey in a dinghy

2. **15 September** The dinghy lands in the Cape Prasso area of Samos. The Greek coastguard are in the area, and witnesses report hearing shots

3. **15 September** 28 members of the group are rescued by the Turkish coastguard, after being put into life rafts and cast adrift by the Greek coastguard

4. **Eight group members** avoid the coastguard and walk inland. Four make it to a refugee camp. Two days later, one further woman is picked up and cast out to sea alone

5. **16 September** Three men, Keita, Kouamou and Ibrahim, are apprehended, put into a speedboat then pushed into the water while out at sea. Ibrahim swims to the shore; Keita and Kouamou do not survive

6. **17 September** Ibrahim is found by the Turkish police, having wandered for 24 hours after washing up on a Turkish beach

7. **18 September** Keita's body is found by the Turkish coastguard

8. **20 September** Kouamou's body is found in the water, close to shore

Guardian graphic

After sleeping in the forest overnight, Keita, Kouamou and another man, Ibrahim*, were apprehended on 16 September.

Ibrahim, a former member of the Cameroonian navy, said they were stopped on a road by people identifying themselves as police officers. They were asked for ID and stripped of their phones and money before being put into a car and taken to a port. Ibrahim said they were then loaded on to a speedboat, which he identified as a Rafnar, a vessel used by the coastguard on Samos.

After half an hour, the boat stopped and Ibrahim says that, one by one, the men were pushed into the water. "I resisted," he said. "They beat me properly before throwing me into the water." He said he swam desperately, the waves helping push him towards the Turkish shore and on to the beach a few hours from Kusadasi. He said he cried out thanks to God before vomiting.

> **I feel like I left a part of me in the water**
> **Ibrahim**

According to Ibrahim, Keita's body washed up soon after. Friends said neither Keita nor Kouamou could swim. Ibrahim tried resuscitation but it was too late. Ibrahim planted a stick in the sand next to Keita's body and started walking along the coast.

He was picked up by Turkish police on 18 September, and described to them the events which led to Keita's death. "They pushed all of us into the sea," he told the authorities. "They did not provide us with a raft or boat." He said Kouamou had disappeared beneath the waves.

Later that day, Keita's body was found by the Turkish coastguard. Two days later, they found Kouamou on the same beach. Ibrahim later identified both bodies in the morgue in Izmir. Medical documents state that Keita drowned and that Kouamou's body had been found in the sea, close to shore.

While it is impossible to fully verify Ibrahim's story, two Greek officials with direct knowledge of coastguard operations, who spoke on condition of anonymity, confirmed that what he described had happened before, usually to smaller groups of asylum seekers. The rationale is to avoid using life rafts, which are expensive; any public tender for their replacement might raise questions. Both officials said refugees are usually provided with lifejackets before being told to swim back to Turkey.

Greece accused of 'biggest pushback in years' of stricken refugee ship

Read more

Since December, the Turkish coastguard have recorded 11 rescues of people in similar circumstances.

Over tea in Izmir in October, Ibrahim said he believed it was partly down to God that he survived. "The sea is my friend, I have no fear," he said. He has since made it back to Greece, where he has registered as a minor. The Guardian cannot verify his age. Months later, he is still haunted by what happened. "I feel like I left a part of me in the water," he said.

Dimitris Choulis, a HRLP lawyer, is filing a lawsuit pressing for criminal charges to be brought against those involved in the pushback on behalf of some of the 36 people who made that journey on 15 September. "What is very dangerous for our democracy is having police officers overstepping the law," he said. "My hope is, as a Greek lawyer, to restore the rule of law in the island of Samos, because this is what seems to have been lost."

Lorraine Leete, from the Legal Centre Lesbos, added: "Pushbacks constitute atrocities against the humankind for which Greece and the EU will have to respond sooner or later, given the hard and accumulated evidence of crimes committed at their borders."

Kouamou's body was returned to Cameroon, thanks to savings from his older brother, Séverin. He leaves behind a wife and two young children. "The news of his death broke us all," said his aunt, Marinette. "His death left me traumatised to have lost such a good son."

Keita's family could not raise the money to bring him back to Ivory Coast, and he lies in an unmarked grave in Izmir, thousands of miles from home.

In a statement, the Greek police authorities said: “The Hellenic police authorities, following a strict disciplinary legal framework, investigate every piece of information which is communicated to them and concerns alleged incidents of ill treatment at the borders, including allegations for unprocessed returns (pushbacks), in order that the foreseen by law penalties are imposed and similar behaviours are avoided in the future. The allegations on the breach of the principle of non-refoulement do not meet reality and in fact undermine the work of the Hellenic police at the operational border areas.”

The Hellenic Coast Guard said in a statement: “The practices described and attributed to operational assets and personnel of the coastguard do not correspond with our operational processes in deterring non-authorised border crossings, or dealing with third country nationals during the surveillance of sea borders.”

**Names have been changed*

Your arms full, and your hair wet, I could not
Speak, and my eyes failed, I was neither
Living nor dead, and I knew nothing,
Looking into the heart of light, the silence.
*Oed' und leer das Meer.*

Turkey seen from Greece, Psili Ammos,
Samos, 28 May 2022

Greece seen from Turkey, Buyuk
Menderes National Park, 30 May 2022

France seen from Switzerland, 3 May 2022

And their friends, the loitering heirs of City directors;
Departed, have left no addresses.
By the waters of Leman I sat down and wept . . .
Sweet Thames, run softly till I end my song,
Sweet Thames, run softly, for I speak not loud or long.

By the rivers of Babylon,
There we sat down, yea, we wept

Unreal City
Under the brown fog of a winter noon
Mr. Eugenides, the Smyrna merchant
Unshaven, with a pocket full of currants

Cracks and reforms and bursts in the violet air
Falling towers
Jerusalem Athens Alexandria
Vienna London
Unreal

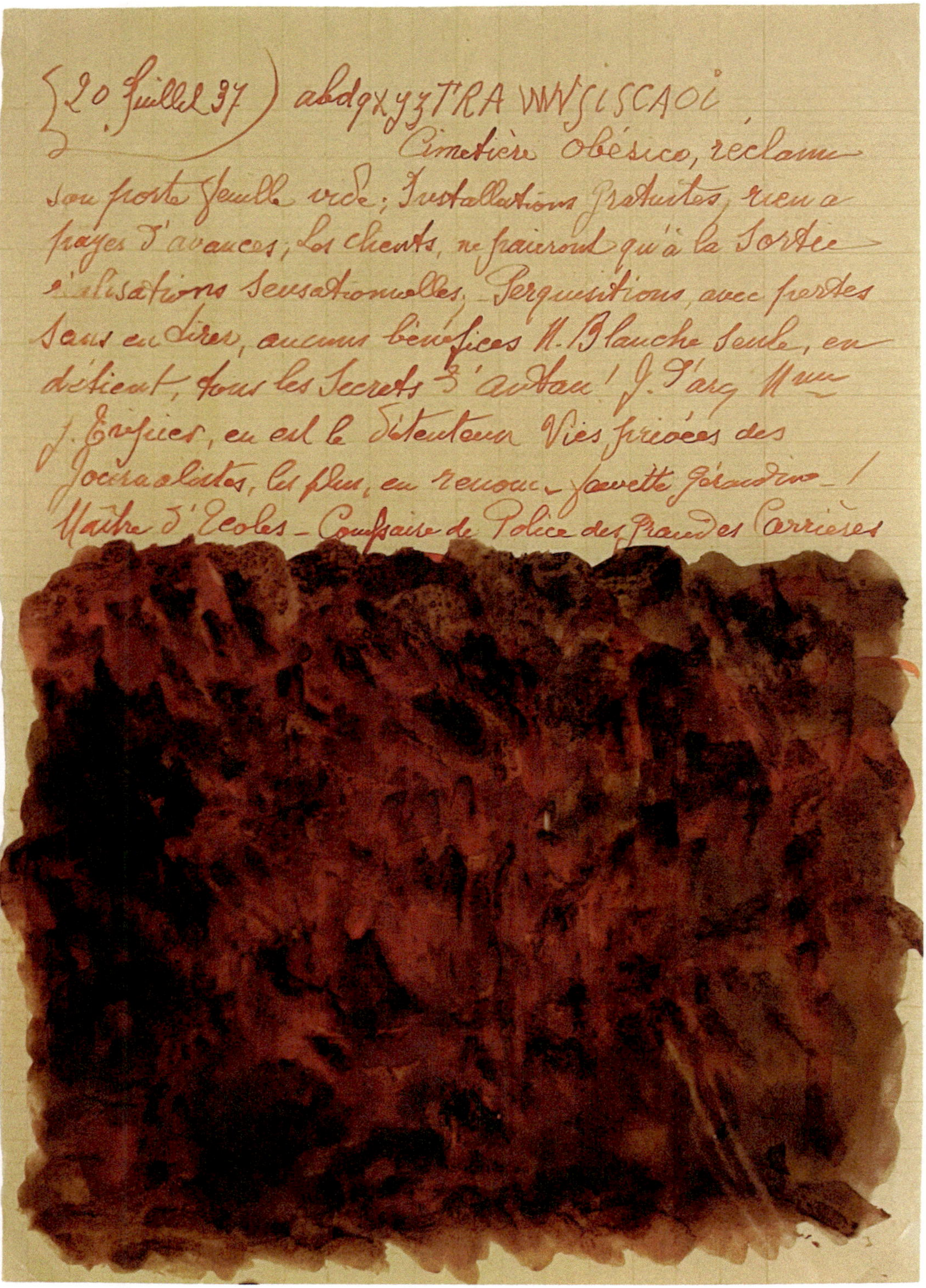
(20 Juillet 37) abdqxyzzTRA VVVVſiSCAOi
Cimetière obésico, réclame
son poste feuille vide; Installations gratuites, rien a
payer d'avances; Les clients, ne paieront qu'à la sortie
réalisations sensationnelles, Perquisitions, avec pertes
sans en tirer, aucuns bénéfices M. Blanche seule, en
détient, tous les secrets d'antan! J. d'arg Mme
J. Ervfier, en est le détenteur Vies privées des
Journalistes, les plus, en renom _ Javette Gérandière _!
Maître d'Ecoles _ Commissaire de Police des Grandes Carrières

Force des prières et [illegible]

Hotel Elite (formerly Hotel Sainte-Luce), Lausanne, 5 May 2022

Elito

almost

young

perhaps

smoking

sling

time

finishing

strangers

know

one

child

broke

back

rough

visit

unreal

Lausanne, 5 May 2022

allowswallowswallowswallowswallowswallowswallowswallowswallowswallowswall

wswallowswallowswallowswallowswallowswallowswallowswallowswallow

which fire?
which train disaster?
which earthquake?
which atrocity?
which border?

*allowswallowswallowswallowswallowswallowswallowswallowswallowswal*

*lowswallowswallowswallowswallowswallowswallowswallowswallowswallowswallow*

falling down falling down

*Poi s'ascose nel foco che gli affina*

*Quando fiam uti chelidon*—O swallow swallow

C'est moi qui vole maintenant
C'est moi qui vole
Les oiseaux ils sont là, c'est moi qui vole

*vallowswallowswallowswallowswallowswallowswallowswallowswallowswa*

I'm the one flying now
I'm the one flying
The birds are there, but i'm the one flying

*llowswallowswallowswallowswallowswallowswallowswallowswallowswallo*

*Quando fiam uti chelidon*—O swallow swallow

*Le Prince d'Aquitaine à la tour abolie*
These fragments I have shored against my ruins

London Bridge is falling down falling down falling down
*Poi s'ascose nel foco che gli affina*
*Quando fiam uti chelidon*—O swallow swallow
*Le Prince d'Aquitaine à la tour abolie*
These fragments I have shored against my ruins

“An earthquake with a moment magnitude of 7.0 occurred on 30 October 2020 about 14 km (8.7 mi) northeast of the Greek island of Samos. Although Samos was closest to the epicentre, it was the Turkish city İzmir, 70 km (43 mi) northeast that was heavily affected—more than 700 residential and commercial structures were seriously damaged or destroyed ... The event is called the Samos earthquake by the International Seismological Centre.”
(Wikipedia)

Vathy, Samos, 24 May 2022

The river's tent is broken; the last fingers of leaf
Clutch and sink into the wet bank. The wind
Crosses the brown land, unheard. The nymphs are de-
parted.

look.
Hurry up please its time
If you don't like it you can get on with it, I said.
Others can pick and choose if you can't.
But if Albert makes off, it won't be for lack of telling.
You ought to be ashamed, I said, to look so antique.

Vathy, Samos, 24 May 2022

ΚΑΠΕΤΑΝ
ΛΑΧΑΝΑ
ΟΔΟΣ
ΣΤΑΜΑΤΙΟΥ
ΓΕΡΟΓΙΑΝΝΑΚ

Vathy Samos 24 May 2022

HURRY UP PLEASE ITS TIME
HURRY UP PLEASE ITS TIME
Goonight Bill. Goonight Lou. Goonight May. Goonight.
Ta ta. Goonight. Goonight.
Good night, ladies, good night, sweet ladies, good night,
good night.

ΓΕΡΟΝΤΗΣ
ELECTRIC
ΜΕΤΑΦΕΡΘΗΚΑΜΕ
ΠΙΣΩ ΑΠΟ ΤΗΝ
ΕΘΝΙΚΗ ΤΡΑΠΕΖΑ.
ΠΡΩΗΝ ΧΡΥΣΟΧΟΕΙΟ
ΣΤΑΥΡΙΝΟΥ.

'Nam Sibyllam quidem Cumis ego ipse oculis meis vidi in ampulla pendere, et cum illi pueri dicerent: *Σίβυλλα τί θέλεις*; respondebat illa: *ἀποθανεῖν θέλω*.'

I saw with my own eyes the Sibyl at Cumae hanging in a cage, and when the boys said to her: "Sibyl, what do you want?" she answered: "I want to die."

The scene Eliot uses for the Epigraph of *The Waste Land* is from the Satyricon. Only fragments still exist. The Sibyl of Cumae was a prophetess in service to Apollo, and a great beauty. Apollo wished to take her as his lover and offered her anything she desired. She asked to live for as many years as there were grains in a handful of dust. Apollo granted her wish, but still she refused to become his lover. She ended up living for hundreds of years, each year becoming smaller and frailer, Apollo having given her long life but not eternal youth.

Central Station, Milan, 9 May 2022

PARTENZE
-From the root.
-Yes.

Havra Sokagi, Izmir, 31 May 2022

Kokari, Samos, 28 May 2022

Vathy Samos 24 May 2022

Vathy, Samos, 24 May 2022

HElp ME!!!

Vathy, Samos, 24 May 2022

HELP ME!!!
Help me

2018

"darting to and fro over the sea. Ceaselessly emitting their tiny cries, they sped along their flightpaths faster than my eyes could follow them. At earlier times, in the summer evenings during my childhood when I had watched from the valley as swallows circled in the last light, still in great numbers in those days, I would imagine that the world was held together by the courses they flew through the air.

…

The sand martins, I now saw, were flying solely at the level that extended from the top of the cliff where I was sitting out into empty space. Not one of them climbed higher or dived lower, to the water below them. Whenever they came towards me, fast as bullets, some seemed to vanish right beneath my feet, as if into the very ground. I went to the edge of the cliff and saw that they had dug their nesting holes into the topmost layer of clay, one beside the other. I was thus standing on perforated ground, as it were, which might have given way at any moment."

*The Rings of Saturn*, WG Sebald (1998)

2018

MANUFRANC
HIRONDELL
SAINT-ETIENNE

Vathy port, Samos, 24 May 2022

GUARDIA di FINANZA
FRONTEX

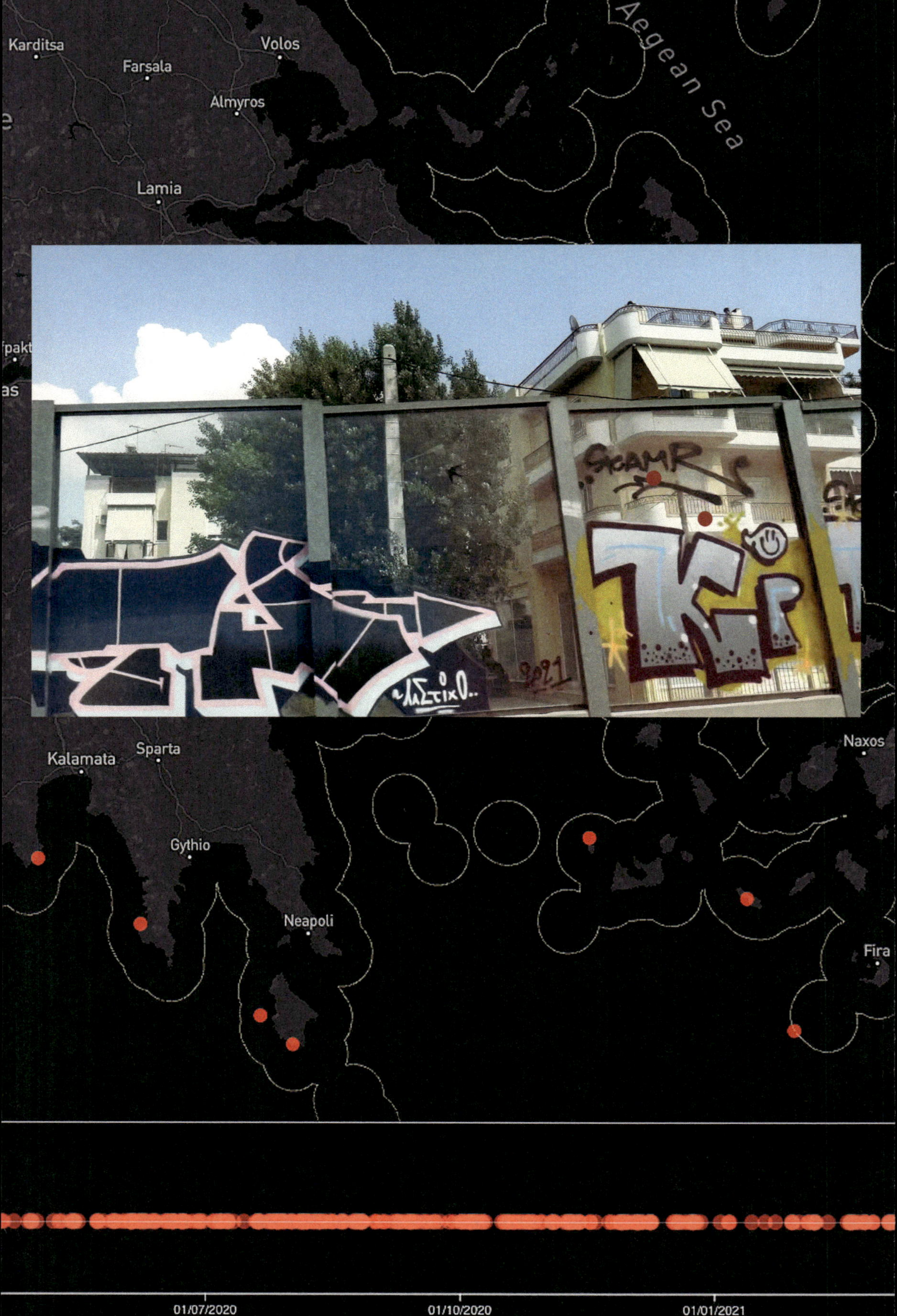
Karditsa
Volos
Farsala
Almyros
Aegean Sea
Lamia
Kalamata
Sparta
Naxos
Gythio
Neapoli
Fira
01/07/2020
01/10/2020
01/01/2021

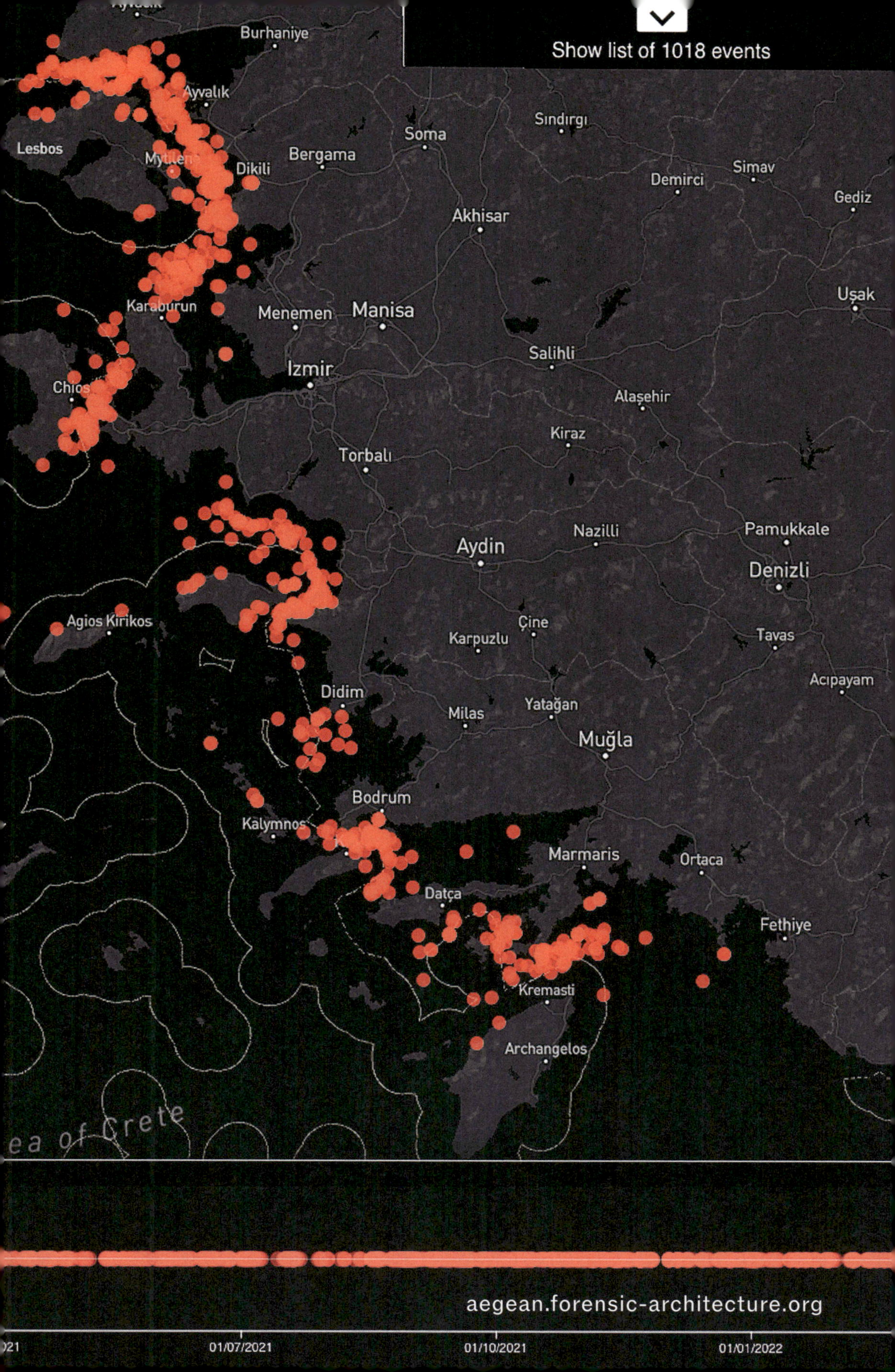

Show list of 1018 events
Burhaniye
Ayvalık
Lesbos
Mytilene
Dikili
Bergama
Soma
Sındırgı
Simav
Demirci
Gediz
Akhisar
Karaburun
Menemen
Manisa
Uşak
Salihli
Izmir
Chios
Alaşehir
Kiraz
Torbalı
Nazilli
Pamukkale
Aydin
Denizli
Agios Kirikos
Çine
Karpuzlu
Tavas
Acıpayam
Didim
Milas
Yatağan
Muğla
Bodrum
Kalymnos
Marmaris
Ortaca
Datça
Fethiye
Kremasti
Archangelos
Sea of Crete
aegean.forensic-architecture.org
01/07/2021
01/10/2021
01/01/2022

From 'is' to 'was'

On the French Wikipedia, I read that "Jeanne Tripier is an artist known for..." Using the present tense, 'is', to describe someone long dead seems strange to me, but I'm told that's the way it is in French according to the rules of 'tense harmony.' On the English site, it's noticeable how, on their death, a person's state is quickly updated from 'is' to 'was'—a grim task that I've somehow always imagined being carried out by the same lone contributor.

by Jeanne Tripier (Musée de l'Art Brut, Lausanne)

Juillet 37 ) abdqXyzIRA VVVSLSCAOC

Cimetière obésico, réclame
porte feuille vide; Installations gratuites, rien a
d'avances; Les clients, ne paieront qu'à la Sortie →
sations sensationnelles. _ Perquisitions, avec pertes
en lires, aucuns bénéfices M. Blanche seule, en
ent, tous les Secrets d'autan! J. d'arg Mme
fices, en est le détenteur Vies privées des
naalistes, les plus, en renom _ fauvette gérandin _ !
re d'Ecoles _ Commissaire de Police des Grandes Carrières

broken

stranger

bitter

queen

forced

pips

leaving

blossom

Thessaloniki cathedral, 19 May 2022

I had not thought death had undone so many.
Sighs, short and infrequent, were exhaled,
And each man fixed his eyes before his feet.

Thessaloniki, 19 May 2022

And water

What is that sound high in the air
Murmur of maternal lamentation
Who are those hooded hordes swarming
Over endless plains, stumbling in cracked earth
Ringed by the flat horizon only
What is the city over the mountains
Cracks and reforms and bursts in the violet air
Falling towers
Jerusalem Athens Alexandria
Vienna London
Unreal

"It is indeed a tombstone... here's the part
I can understand: a respectful wise woman.
Speaks true words..."
(SMS from a friend, regarding p 110)

Spread out in fiery points
Glowed into words, then would be savagely still.

'My nerves are bad to-night. Yes, bad. Stay with me.
Speak to me. Why do you never speak? Speak.
    What are you thinking of? What thinking? What?
I never know what you are thinking. Think.'

I think we are in rats' alley
Where the dead men lost their bones.

'What is that noise?'

Then spoke the thunder
Da
*Datta*: what have we given?
My friend, blood shaking my heart
The awful daring of a moment's surrender
Which an age of prudence can never retract
By this, and this only, we have existed

At the violet hour, when the eyes and back
Turn upward from the desk, when the human engine waits
Like a taxi throbbing waiting,

And fiddled whisper music on those strings
And bats with baby faces in the violet light
Whistled, and beat their wings
And crawled head downward down a blackened wall
And upside down in air were towers
Tolling reminiscent bells, that kept the hours

Monasteriotes Synagogue, Thessaloniki, 22 May 2022

corridor
between
days

Who is the third who walks always beside you?
When I count, there are only you and I together
But when I look ahead up the white road
There is always another one walking beside you
Gliding wrapt in a brown mantle, hooded
I do not know whether a man or a woman
—But who is that on the other side of you?

Thessaloniki 22 May 2022

Vathy, Samos, 24 May 2022

Karataş, Izmir, 30 May 2022

Inside Alpha Land, one of two community centres
run by Samos Volunteers, 26 May 2022

Mouth Piece (2018, pp. 12–25) involved a poring-over of the recordings we'd made during a week of random hitch-hiking in Germany. As we studied the sounds in granular detail, attempting to absorb them through learning, we started to understand the full extent of what people had said to us; not just the meaning, but something of the psychology behind their words. Following this journey to Izmir I fell into a similarly retrospective, forensic, approach, but involving photography this time more than voice.

Discovering Moyra Davey's essay *Notes on Photography & Accident*, excerpts of which are included here, helped me understand what I was doing. It's comprised in large part of short quotes by other people: Walter Benjamin, Susan Sontag, Roland Barthes and others.

"The viewer [of the photograph] feels an irresistible compulsion to seek the tiny spark of accident, the here and now." (Benjamin)

Travelling alone, I took photographs as a means of defence by deferral, flinging affect into the future: so often, the here-and-now felt saturated, too much to cope with. Going over the images later and making sense of things through writing became, it seems, the second part of this survival process—an attempt at collecting and connecting these "tiny sparks" into a redemptive constellation.

Havra Sokagi, Izmir, 21 May 2022

Davey writes that "Benjamin ... was interested in photographs, whose aesthetic qualities were secondary, a by-product of some other intention or drive. At the end of Camera Lucida, Barthes declares that photography as art is worthless to him because it's not mad. Only an original, mad work will pitch the viewer right back into what he calls 'the very letter of Time,' the wound of Time, the sense of loss that in turn produces for Barthes 'a photographic ecstasy'."

"Photographs are, of course, artefacts. But their appeal is that they also seem, in a world littered with photographic relics, to have the status of found objects" (Susan Sontag).

Finding them on my phone later, some of the photos seem to be taken by the person who was missing. One thing for certain: at times, I didn't know what I was doing.

"It is through photography that we first discover the existence of [the] optical unconscious, just as we discover the instinctual unconscious through psychoanalysis" (Janet Malcolm).

Havra Sokagi, Izmir, 31 May 2022

Algazi Sinagogu
Algazi Sinagogue
KONAK BELEDİYESİ
2015

HEVRA
SiNAGOGU

Almanya
Federal Cumhuriyeti Başkonsolosluğu
İzmir
Conservation measures for the Hevra-Synagogue were carried out with financial support from the Consulate General of Germany in Izmir.
Hevra Sinagogunda alınan koruma önlemleri
Almanya İzmir Başkonsolosluğu'nun mali desteğiyle gerçekleştirilmiştir.

Tent village near Temple of Hephaestus, Athens, 1922

What are the roots that clutch, what branches grow
Out of this stony rubbish? Son of man,
You cannot say, or guess, for you know only
A heap of broken images, where the sun beats,
... gives no shelter, the cricket no relief,

Zervou refugee camp, Samos, 26 May 2022

Sent from inside the Zervou refugee camp, Samos, 16 July 2022

guess, for you know only
A heap of broken images, where the sun beats,
And the dead tree gives no shelter, the cricket no relief,
And the dry stone no sound of water. Only
There is shadow under this red rock,
(Come in under the shadow of this red rock),
And I will show you something different from either
Your shadow at morning striding behind you

Or your shadow at evening rising to meet you;
I will show you fear in a handful of dust.

Samos, 26 May 2022

hiding

again

already

basket

without

unable

watch

don't

cry

to

death

a.h. (You)

And upside down in air were towers
Tolling reminiscent bells, that kept the hours
And voices singing out of empty cisterns and exhausted
wells.

In this decayed hole among the mountains
In the faint moonlight, the grass is singing
Over the tumbled graves

"Dogancay cemetery,
cemetery of the nameless
The wooden plaque is
numbered 68091 - no
name"

16595

59515
59518

68003

SU ARAS
BEBEK
ÇELİK

GÜZEL KIZIM
SU ARAS
BEBEK
ÇELİK

Karataş, Izmir, 30 May 2022

Karatas, Izmir, 30 May 2022

displayed
As though a window gave upon the sylvan scene
The change of Philomel, by the barbarous king
So rudely forced; yet there the nightingale
Filled all the desert with inviolable voice
And still she cried, and still the world pursues,
'Jug Jug' to dirty ears.
And other withered stumps of time
Were told upon the walls; staring forms

Karataş, Izmir, 30 May 2022

Copy
Select All
Look Up
Anlatirken Seni
Birden Bozulur
Diksiyonum
SUDE
Dilek

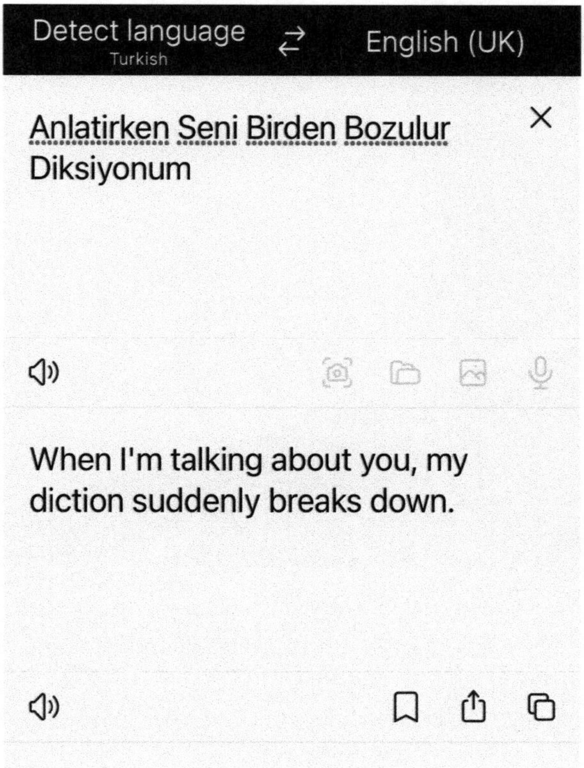
Detect language
Turkish
English (UK)
Anlatirken Seni Birden Bozulur Diksiyonum
When I'm talking about you, my diction suddenly breaks down.

At the violet hour, when the eyes and back
Turn upward from the desk, when the human engine waits
Like a taxi throbbing waiting,
I Tiresias, though blind, throbbing between two lives,
Old man with wrinkled female breasts, can see
At the violet hour, the evening hour that strives
Homeward, and brings the sailor home from sea,
The typist home at teatime, clears her breakfast, lights
Her stove, and lays out food in tins.
Out of the window perilously spread
Her drying combinations touched by the sun's last rays,
On the divan are piled (at night her bed)
Stockings, slippers, camisoles, and stays.

Karataş, Izmir, 31 May 2022

"An adversarial stance, maintaining a relation with the work, but arguing with it. This means we avoid two kinds of silence—the coercive silence of censorship, and the passive silence of the submissive reader."

And here is the one-eyed merchant, and this card,
Which is blank, is something he carries on his back,
Which I am forbidden to see. I do not find
The Hanged Man. Fear death by water.
I see crowds of people, walking round in a ring.

## *IV. Death by Water*

Phlebas the Phoenician, a fortnight dead,
Forgot the cry of gulls, and the deep sea swell
And the profit and loss.

A current under sea
Picked his bones in whispers. As he rose and fell
He passed the stages of his age and youth
Entering the whirlpool.

Gentile or Jew

rd,
tall as you.

Don't think, don't think

and don't

in all life is based on

on change everything cha

the house other than th

changes anything changes the

say anything in this non

that You drink it big, it w

You consumed it. Ever

changes. It changes.

in this reality. You h

This planet is based on

in these things. G

I hope

don't think about water

get wet

change this planet is built

es the house other than

person changes everything

ruler and changes everything

polar planet the water

l break. Change you are in it.

thing on this planet

You have to be happy

e to accept this time.

change. You have to believe

d luck, God willing,

you call

Τις καταστροφές στις πόλεις και τα χωριά απ' όπου περάσαμε, τους εμπρησμούς και τις άλλες ασχημίες, δεν είμαι ικανός **να περιγράψω και προτιμώ να μείνουν στη λήθη.**

The devastation of the cities and villages through which we passed, the arsons and other ugliness, I am not able to describe, **and I prefer that the world remains oblivious to it.**

198

The Turks enter Smyrna on September 9, 1922, "actually firing on British and American ships engaged in rescue work". [87] Determined to destroy completely "Giaour-Izmir", the "Infidel Smyrna", they set fire to the whole city. Reading eye-witness reports in the different newspapers one is overwhelmed by the gigantic catastrophe. Mr. Ward Price telegraphs to the *Daily Mail* :

> *What I see as I stand on the deck of the* Iron Duke *is an unbroken wall of fire, two miles long, in which twenty distinct volcanoes of raging flames are throwing up jagged, writhing tongues to a height of a hundred feet... From this intensely glowing mass of yellow, orange and crimson fire pour up thick clotted coils of oily black smoke that hide the moon at its zenith... The sea glows a deep copper-red, and, worst of all, from the densely packed mob of many thousands of refugees huddled on the narrow quay, between the advancing fiery death behind and the deep water in front, comes continuously such frantic screaming of sheer terror as can be heard miles away.*[88]

84. The author does not wish to give the impression that all the outrages and persecutions during the campaign were due to the Turkish Army. The war was an exceptionally ravaging one and numerous atrocities were committed on both sides. To a great degree the inhumanity exhibited by the Turks after the Sakaria defeat was prompted by the previous uncivilized behavior of the Greek Army. (See General Staff of the Western Front, Second Section, *Greek Atrocities in Asia Minor* (Constantinople : Husy-i-Tabiat Printing House, 1922). As, however, the chapter deals with the creation of the refugee problem, these facts, the fate of the unredeemed Christians is emphasized.

| | |
|---|---|
| Recitar! Mentre preso dal delirio | "Act! While in delirium, |
| non so più quel che dico | I no longer know what I say |
| e quel che faccio! | or what I do! |
| Eppur è d'uopo, sforzati! | And yet it's necessary. Force yourself! |
| Bah! Sei tu forse un uom? | Bah! Are you even a man?" |

She smooths her hair with automatic hand,
And puts a record on the gramophone.

'This music crept by me upon the waters'

“as foreign sailors could see through their binoculars, Smyrniots were robbed, set on fire, clubbed to death, or pushed into the sea by soldiers and irregulars. So many corpses clogged the sea that if you fell in you might not sink. Some sailors tried shooting at corpses to make them sink.”

Burning burning burning burning
O Lord Thou pluckest me out
O Lord Thou pluckest

burning

Inexplicable splendour of Ionian white and gold.

The river sweats
Oil and tar

a s d a y

Nothing again nothing.

'Do

You know nothing? Do you see nothing? Do you remember

'Nothing?'

I remember

Those are pearls that were his eyes.

'Are you alive, or not? Is there nothing in your head?'

But

DINOSAURS

TRUST UNDERATED
FUTURE
TRUST UNDERATED

DINOSAURS
ROAR!

The same book being read in Athens (2022)
and in the Eurotunnel (2012)

These fragments I have shared against my ruins

These fragments I have shored against my ruins